GW00390948

Playing Piano Is Fun

Alice Chua

Book 4

Student: _____ Alexis & Olivia LAM

Teacher: _____ Ms ALICE CHUA

© RHYTHM MP SDN. BHD. 2012

Published by
RHYTHM MP SDN. BHD.
1947, Lorong IKS Bukit Minyak 2,
Taman IKS Bukit Minyak, 14100 Simpang Ampat,
Penang, Malaysia.
Tel: +60 4 5050246 (Direct Line), +60 4 5073690 (Hunting Line)
Fax: +60 4 5050691
E-mail: rhythmmp@mphsb.com
Website: www.rhythmmp.com

ISBN 10: 967-985-619-4
ISBN 13: 978 967985619 4
Order No.: MPP-4003-04

Rhythm MP

Foreword

Playing Piano is Fun is a keyboard tutor series for beginners. It is designed to meet the developmental needs of children as they journey through the wonderful world of music. The tunes are specially composed by Alice Chua, and are based on the characters and subjects from the classic stories of *Alice's Adventures in Wonderland* and *Through the Looking-Glass* by Lewis Carroll. The literary experience is translated into the language of music with the intention of awakening the musical interests of children.

Playing Piano is Fun is a novel approach developed through the author's practical experience derived from teacher-pupil interaction. The large music font size captures the students' attention and helps them to focus. Meanwhile, pages are left intentionally without pictures to encourage students to further express their creativity by providing illustrations for the songs themselves. New elements are introduced incrementally and are incorporated progressively. Teacher's accompaniment is encouraged to enhance the musical experience, thus inspiring and motivating students. Some suggestions for the enhancement of the teaching elements can be found inside the front cover. In addition to playing piano, this series' unique approach includes listening, singing, transposing, harmonising, improvising and composing at an early stage.

A note from the author:

I wish pupils and teachers many fun and enjoyable music-making sessions with this series.

Yours musically,

Alice Chua, MA, FLCM, LLCM, Adv Dip Kodaly, Yamaha Teaching Cert. Grade 3.

About the Author

Alice is a passionate and enthusiastic musician, a versatile arranger, composer and music author. To this date, she has written many music books, used extensively in Asia and the United Kingdom. She is also an examiner with the London College of Music.

Whilst living in Malaysia and Singapore, Alice was Chief Music Instructor for Yamaha Music Asia. She opened new music schools in Singapore, Malaysia and Myanmar, and started music programs for pre-schoolers in Indonesia. This involved training teachers and designing music curricula suited specifically for each country. She frequently represented Malaysia in various international conferences hosted by Yamaha Music Foundation.

Now residing in London with her daughter, Alice divides her time between sharing her love of music with her students and invigilating examinations and competitions in Europe and the Far East. She believes that music should be played from memory, so that every child has the confidence to perform in any environment at any time, without needing to rely on a score. When children can express themselves freely in this way, it develops their ability to immediately engage their audience, and to derive from the music a personal sense of enjoyment.

Dedication

I would like to dedicate this series to my daughter Mitra and all my students, especially those who have chosen music as their profession.

I look back with fondness on our shared past, revel in our current projects and eagerly anticipate the future.

Contents

The Blue Caterpillar's Rock Dance

Alice Chua

Lively

What is the Caterpillar sitting on?

Draw a blue Caterpillar.

Fun Time 1   Date:

1 **Let's draw treble clefs.**

2 **Write C major scale ascending using semibreves.**

3 **Write C major scale descending using minims.**

Fun Time 2   Date:

1   **Let's draw bass clefs.**

2   **Write C major scale ascending using semibreves.**

3   **Write C major scale descending using crotchets.**

The Magic Mushroom

Alice Chua

What happens to Alice when she eats the magic mushroom?

Draw a magic mushroom.

Fun Time 3

Date:

1   **Write the key signature of G major.**

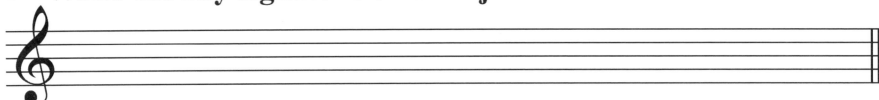

2   **Write the scale of G major ascending using semibreves. Use the correct key signature.**

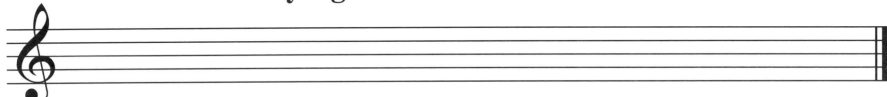

3   **Write the scale of G major descending using quavers. Do not use key signature. Use the correct accidentals.**

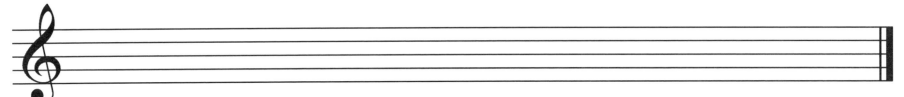

Fun Time 4   Date:

1   **Write the key signature of G major.**

2   **Write the scale of G major ascending using semibreves.
Use the correct key signature.**

3   **Write the scale of G major descending using semiquavers.
Do not use key signature. Use the correct accidentals.**

The Fish-Footman

Alice Chua

Whose message does the Fish-Footman bring to the Duchess?

Draw a man with a Fish mask.

Fun Time 5   Date:

1   **Write the key signature of D major.**

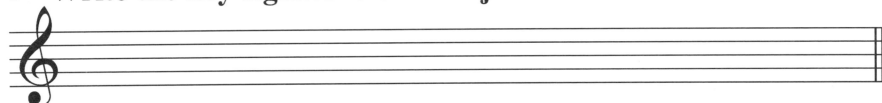

2   **Write the scale of D major ascending using semibreves. Use the correct key signature.**

3   **Write the scale of G major descending using crotchets. Do not use key signature. Use the correct accidentals.**

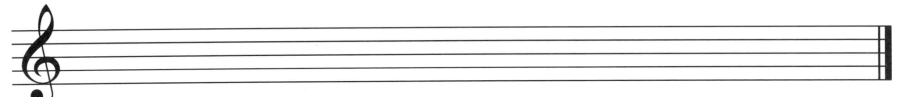

Fun Time 6   Date:

1   **Write the key signature of D major.**

2   **Write the scale of D major ascending using semibreves.**
     Use the correct key signature.

3   **Write the scale of D major descending using minims.**
     Do not use key signature. Use the correct accidentals.

The Frog-Footman

Alice Chua

Who does the Frog-Footman work for?

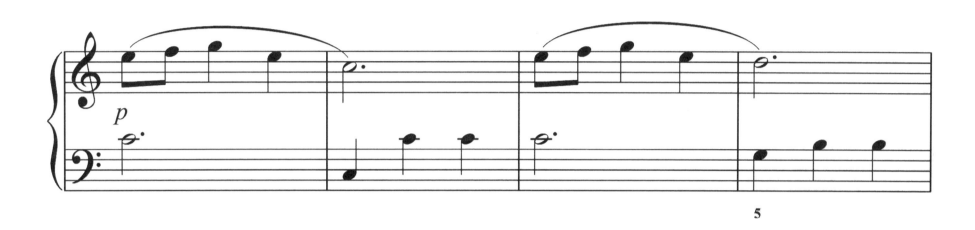

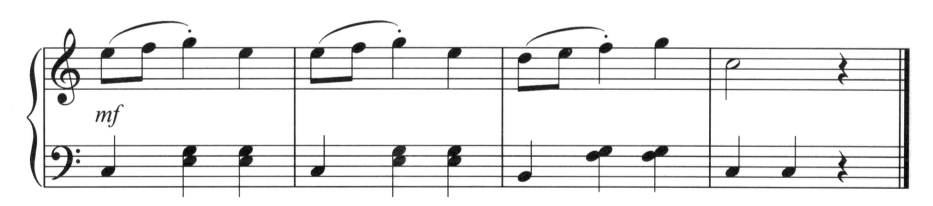

Draw a man with a Frog mask.

Fun Time 7   Date:

1   **Write a semibreve on every line.**

      Write a sharp in front of each note.

2   **Write a semibreve on every line.**

      Write a flat in front of each note.

3   **Write a semibreve on every line.**

      Write a natural in front of each note.

Fun Time 8   **Date:**

1   **Write a minim in every space.**

      Write a sharp in front of each note.

2   **Write a crotchet in every space.**

      Write a flat in front of each note.

3   **Write a quaver in every space.**

      Write a natural in front of each note.

The Sneezing Duchess

Alice Chua

Your teacher will explain quintuplets and tied notes to you.

Draw a pot of peppery soup.

Fun Time 9   Date:

1 **Write a semibreve G note, followed by its rest.**

2 **Write a minim B note, followed by its rest.**

3 **Write a crotchet A note, followed by its rest.**

Fun Time 10   Date:

1   **Write a quaver D note, followed by its rest.**

2   **Write a semiquaver F note, followed by its rest.**

3   **Write the following named rest.**

| Semibreve or bar rest | Minim rest | Crotchet rest | Quaver rest | Semiquaver rest |

The Grinning Cheshire-Cat

Alice Chua

Cheekily

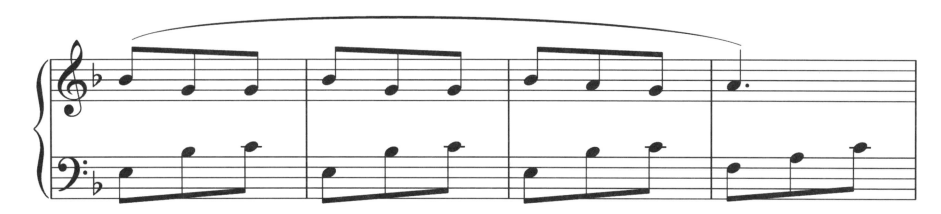

The Cheshire-Cat always grins from _____ to _____ .

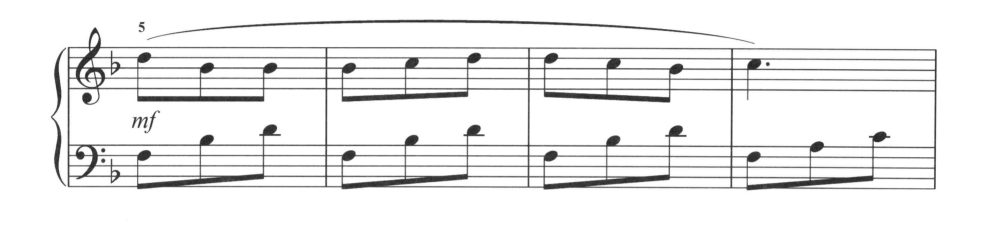

The Cheshire-Cat is grinning cheekily. Can you play all the quavers evenly?

Fun Time 11   Date:

1   **Write the key note of C major followed by the tonic triad.**

2   **Write the key note of C major followed by the tonic triad.**

3   **Write the key note of G major followed by the tonic triad. Use the correct key signature.**

Fun Time 12   Date:

1 **Write the key note of G major followed by the tonic triad.**
Do not use key signature.

2 **Write the key note of G major followed by the tonic triad.**
Use the correct key signature.

3 **Write the key note of G major followed by the tonic triad.**
Do not use key signature.

Alice at the March Hare's Tea Party

Alice Chua

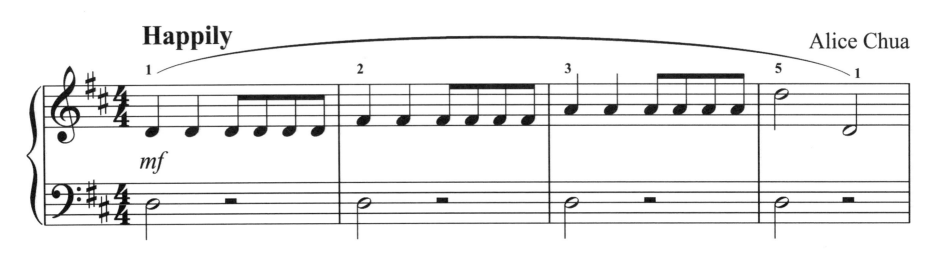

Who is at the tea party?

Fine

D.C. al Fine - to repeat from the beginning and play until *Fine.* *D.C. al Fine*

Fun Time 13   Date:

1 **Write the key note of D major followed by the tonic triad. Use the correct key signature.**

2 **Write the key note of D major followed by the tonic triad. Do not use key signature. Use the necessary accidentals.**

3 **Write the key note of D major followed by the tonic triad. Use the correct key signature.**

Fun Time 14   Date:

1   **Write the key note of D major followed by the tonic triad.**
     Do not use key signature. Use the necessary accidentals.

2   **Write the key note of F major followed by the tonic triad.**
     Use the correct key signature.

3   **Write the key note of F major followed by the tonic triad.**
     Do not use key signature.

Dormouse in the Teapot

Teasingly

Alice Chua

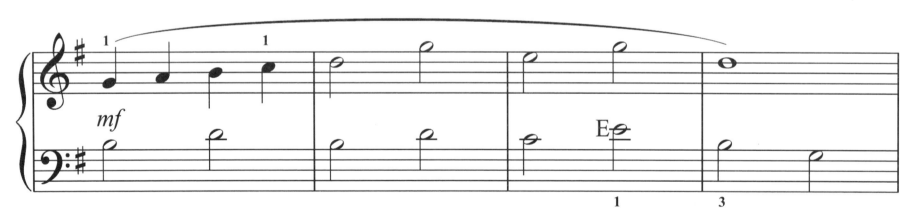

The Teapot song is...."I'm a little teapot, short and stout...."

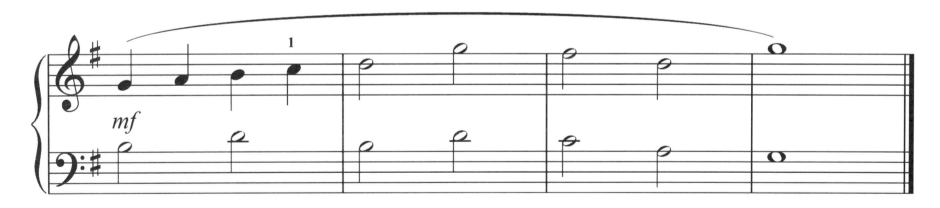

Who is teasing the Dormouse? Draw a teapot.

Fun Time 15   Date:

1   **Write the key signature of G major.**

2   **Write the key signature of D major.**

3   **Write the key signature of F major.**

Fun Time 16   Date:

1 **Write the key signature of G major.**

2 **Write the key signature of D major.**

3 **Write the key signature of F major.**

The Hatter's Special Watch

Alice Chua

Rhythmically

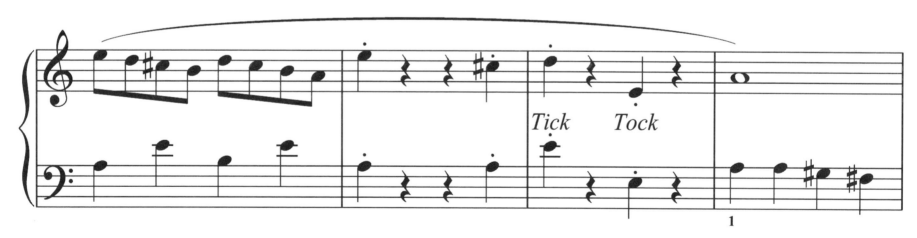

Why is the Hatter's watch special?

Draw the Hatter's watch.

Fun Time 17

Date:

1 **Name the following melodic intervals.**

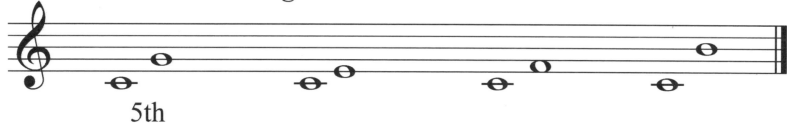

5th

_____ _____ _____ _____

2 **Name the following melodic intervals.**

_____ _____ _____ _____

3 **Name the following melodic intervals.**

_____ _____ _____ _____

Fun Time 18   Date:

1   **Name the following harmonic intervals.**

        4th

_____   _____   _____   _____

2   **Name the following harmonic intervals.**

_____   _____   _____   _____

3   **Name the following harmonic intervals.**

_____   _____   _____   _____

The Queen's Croquet Game

Alice Chua

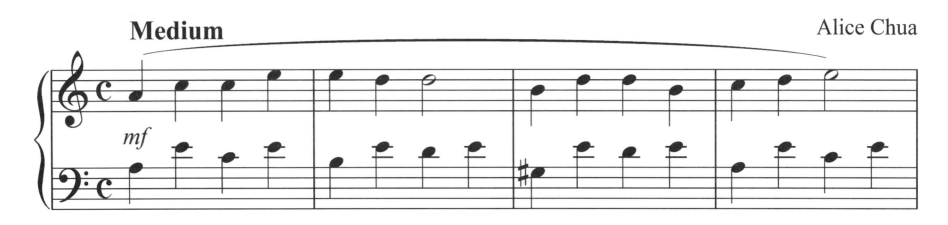

How does the Queen play croquet?

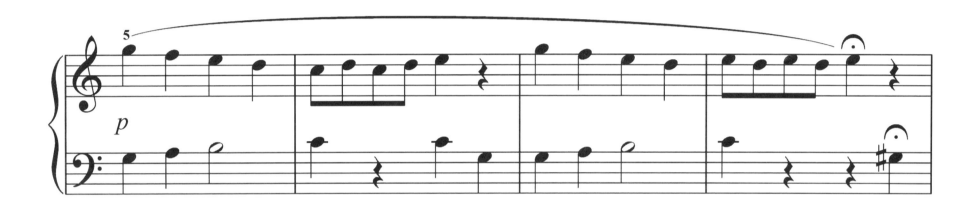

Observe the *fermata* markings at bar 12.
Your teacher will show you how to 'pause' at the markings.

Fun Time 19 Date:

Using the melodic stimuli as the basis of your composition, complete a four-bar phrase. Can you give a title to each of your compositions?

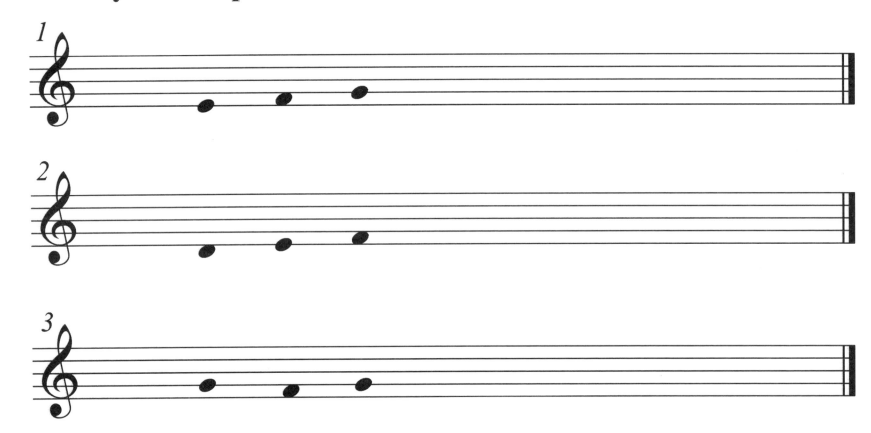

Fun Time 20

Date:

Now answer the given rhythm by clapping a two-bar phrase.

1

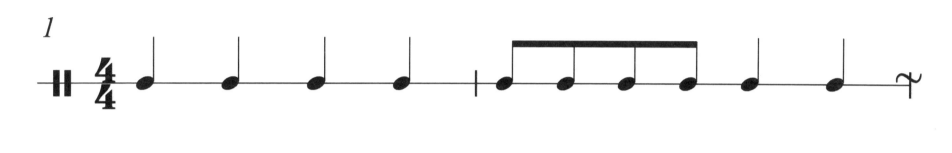

2

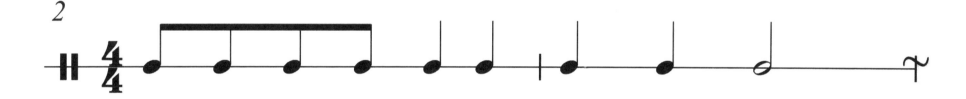

3

The White Rose Tree

Alice Chua

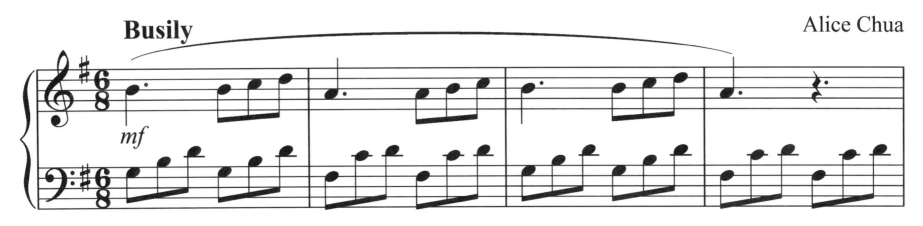

What colour are the guards painting the white rose tree?

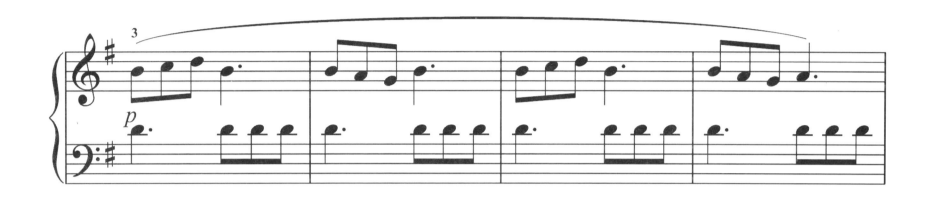

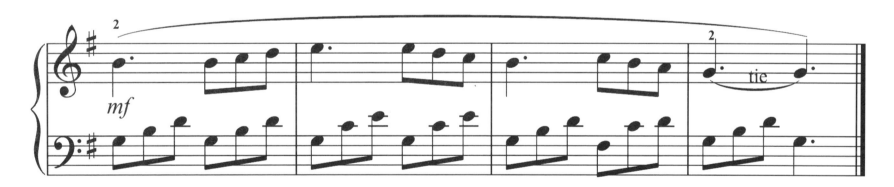

Your teacher will explain tied notes to you.
Draw a red rose tree.

The Soldier's Arch

(Secondo)

Alice Chua

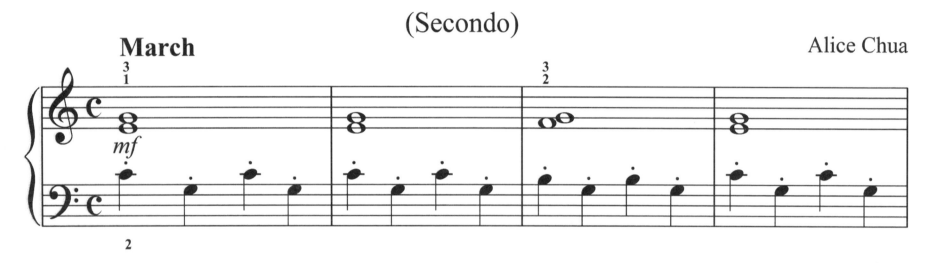

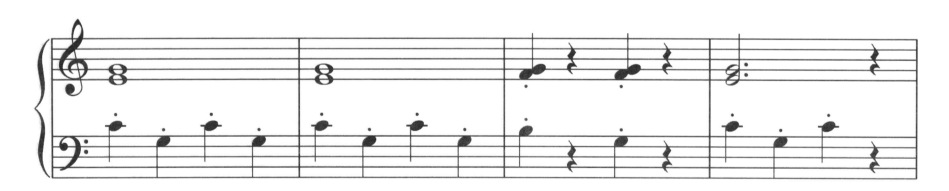

The soldiers are forming an arch for the croquet game.

The Soldier's Arch

(Primo)

Alice Chua

March

Play both hands one octave higher

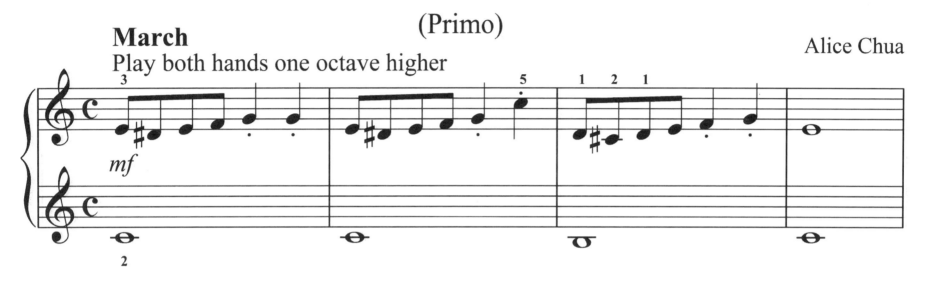

How do the soldiers form an arch?

50

(Secondo)

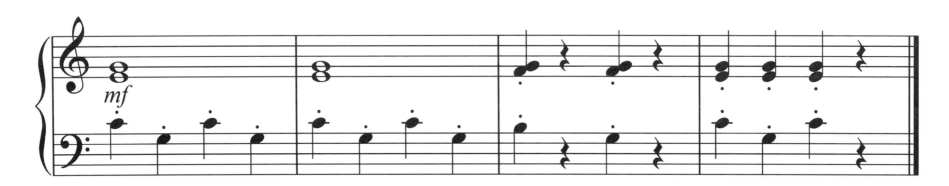

Who appears during the croquet game?

(Primo)

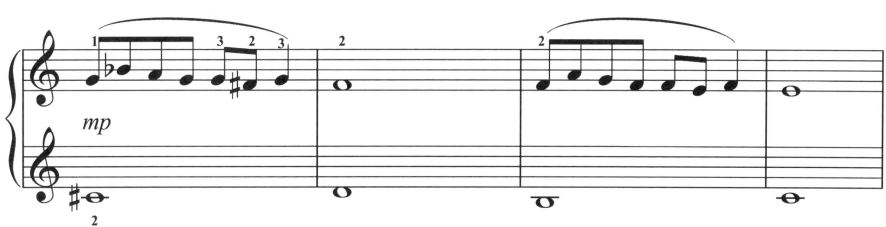

What is special about the Queen's croquet mallets?

The Un-Birthday Song

(Secondo)

Alice Chua

Happily

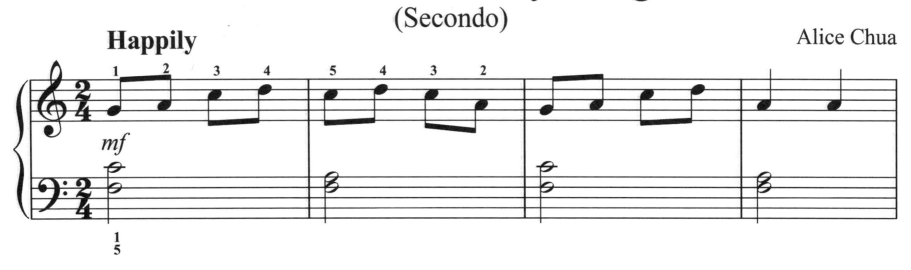

How many Un-Birthdays do you have a year?

The Un-Birthday Song
(Primo)

Happily

Alice Chua

Play both hands two octaves higher

How many Un-Birthday presents can you receive in a year?

(Secondo)

Can you draw an Un-Birthday cake?

(Primo)

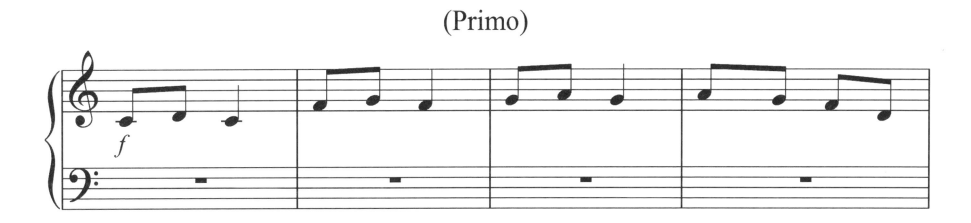

How many candles are on an Un-Birthday cake?

Alice's Keyboard-Game

(Secondo)

Alice Chua

Lively

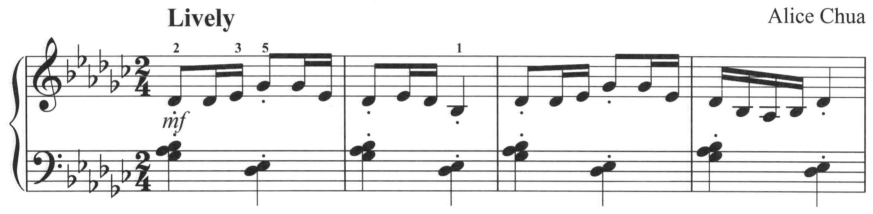

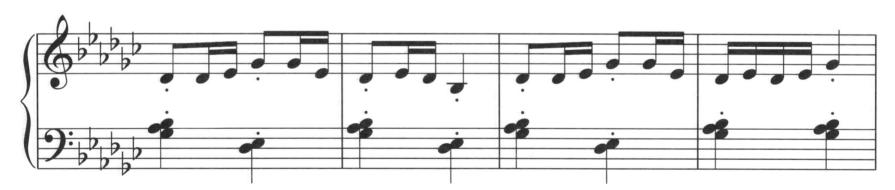

Let's play Keyboard-Game.
Use your fist to play the notes in the bass clef.

Alice's Keyboard-Game

(Primo)

Lively
Play both hands two octaves higher

Alice Chua

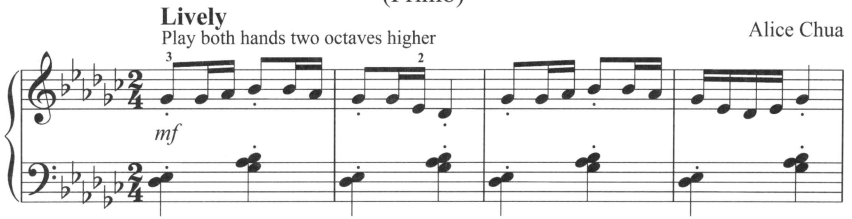

Let's play Keyboard-Game.
Use your fist to play the notes in the bass clef.

(Secondo)

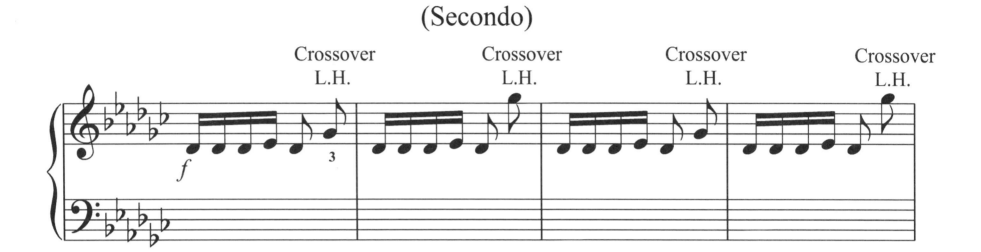

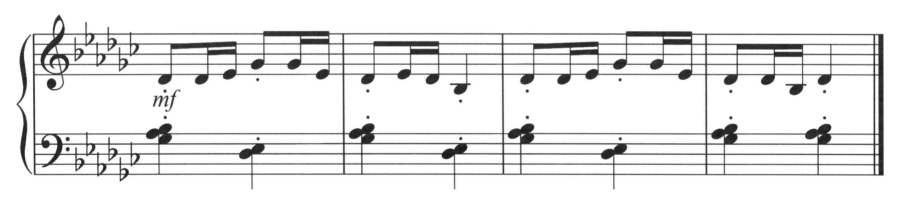

In bars 9-12, your left hand will cross over your right to play the G note.

(Primo)

In bars 10 and 12, your left hand will cross over your right hand to play the D note.

Performance Direction

Direction	Musical Term	Interpretation
f	Forte	Loud
mf	Mezzo forte	Medium loud
mp	Mezzo piano	Medium soft
p	Piano	Soft
⌢	Fermata	Pause and hold the note longer than its original value
♩	Accent	Play the note with emphasis
<	Crescendo	Gradually getting louder
>	Diminuendo	Gradually getting softer